This hoppingly good book belongs to:

For Thomas and Matthew,
my best friend's boys – GC

For Mum and Dad – KC

NorthParadePublishing

4 North Parade,
Bath BA1 1LF. UK
www.nppbooks.co.uk

Snow White AND THE Seven Dart Frogs

Written by Gemma Cary
Illustrated by Kelly Caswell

One day, in a faraway land, another mirror went crashing to the floor.

"**Stupid thing!**" shouted Queenie, stamping her foot.

"Not again, m' lady..." sighed the butler, reaching for the Super Shard Sucker.

"These magic mirrors are maddening!" said Queenie. "None of them will give me the right answer. It's my wretched stepdaughter. Why is she so disgustingly pretty?"

Locked in her room, the wretched stepdaughter heard the commotion.

"Another seven years of bad luck for Queenie," she said. "She must be up to at least **700 years by now!**"

The stepdaughter's name, if you haven't already guessed, was Snow White. It's true, she was extremely pretty. But Snow White wasn't aware of her beauty, and that made her even prettier.

Snow White tapped the large glass tank in her room. A tiny black frog sprang from under a leaf.

Soon, six more frogs appeared. They were poison dart frogs – a gift from her father, the King, before he left on a yoga retreat.

"Darling daughter," he had said, "Did you know that a group of frogs is called an army? Well, this army will always protect you."

Twelve years later, the King still hadn't returned.

The King had also explained to Snow White that, although the frogs were lethal in the wild, they weren't poisonous in captivity. Snow White decided to keep this a secret. So everyone, including Queenie, thought the frogs were absolutely deadly!

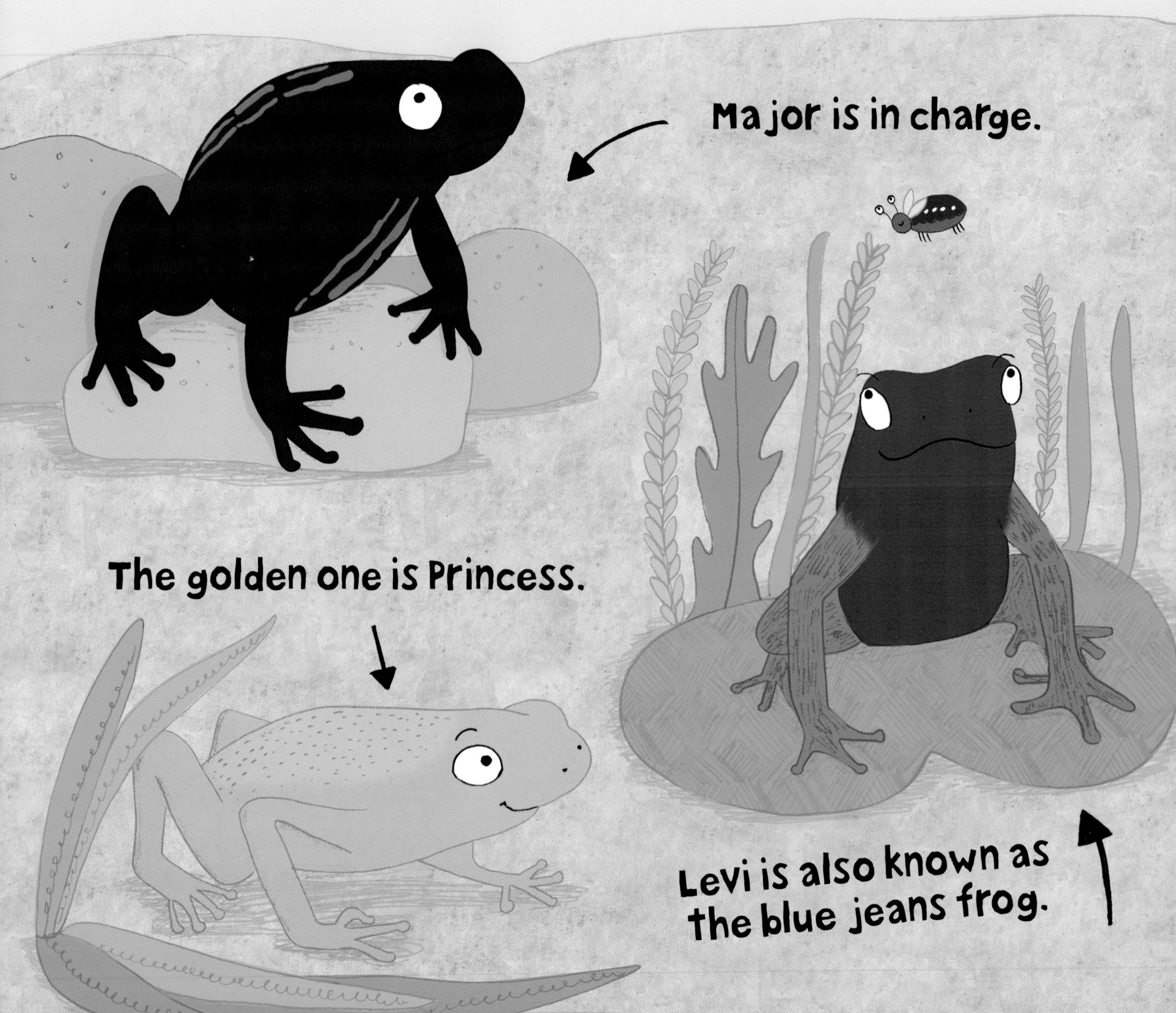

The green, slimy one is Bogie.
Buzz looks like a bumblebee.
Grouch is always moody.
Sweetness is red, like a strawberry.

Jealous of her stepdaughter's beauty (and convinced the frogs were dangerous), Queenie refused to let anyone into Snow White's room. Food was posted through a flap in the door, and toilet duties were carried out in the en suite.

Now, Snow White was one of those little girls who was very good at amusing herself. But even those little girls get bored eventually, especially when they are stuck in one place all day and all night.

So Snow White came up with a cunning escape plan. She began to save the squares of silver foil that covered her meals…

Top secret

One morning, Snow White peered out of her food flap. "Oh, Queenie!" she called. "**I have a new mirror for you!**"

Queenie raced to Snow White's door.

"A mirror?" she panted.
"Is it a magic mirror?"

"Oh yes," said Snow White. "It's the biggest magic mirror you've ever seen. In fact, it's so ginormous, you'll need to come in here to see it."

The curious Queenie unlocked the door. Inside, she was greeted by her reflection in an enormous silvery mirror.

After smoothing her eyebrows with spit, and picking toast from her teeth, Queenie began her usual chant.

"**Mirror, mirror,** on the wall: who's the fairest of them all?"

Snow White spoke in a gruff voice from behind the tank. "**You, my Queen!**" she boomed.

"At last!" Queenie crooned. "I am the most beautiful queen of all! The most beautiful creature! The most beautiful ..."

… **FROG!**"

Snow White released the front of the tank and the foil-covered glass fell to the floor.

The dart frogs leapt onto their target.

Buzz landed on Queenie's **nose**.

Grouch aimed for her **forehead**.

Bogie clung to her **chin**.

"**The frogs!**" squawked Queenie. "The deadly frogs!"

She charged through the palace, swiping at her face.

"**I'm poisoned!**" she wailed. "Done for!"

She hurtled through the gardens, waving her arms like an angry octopus. As she ran towards the palace gates, the frogs jumped into the flowerbeds. But Queenie just carried on running.

Soon she was through the gates and zigzagging across the valley.

Watching from the palace gardens, Snow White slammed the gates. "**It's my turn to lock YOU out!**" she yelled. Then she held out her hands and seven tiny frogs hopped onto her palms.

"Thank you," she said, placing a small kiss on each frog's head.

Suddenly, Princess gave a loud belch. Sweetness and the others did the same. Then, one by one, the seven dart frogs turned into ...

... SEVEN PRINCES!
Hair gel, anyone?
It's me - Buzz!

At your service, Ma'am.
That crazy old bat hit my bad leg!

Snow White and the seven princes became great friends and all lived together in the palace.

"One day," said Snow White, "**I might marry one of you**. But I haven't yet decided which one. To help me decide, you should all be extremely kind and cook for me and do my washing and –"

To this day, Snow White is happily unmarried. The princes live in hope.